P.B. Bear

 cake

 milk

Hilda

 Bob

 Milly

 friends

 box

 hat

 white coat

 stethoscope

ambulance

 bandage

 crutches

medicine

spoon

 x-ray

 hospital

plaster

 biscuit

www.dk.com

Designers   Chris Fraser, Claire Jones
Editors   Joanna Devereux, Fiona Munro
DTP Designer   Jill Bunyan
Photography   Dave King
Production   Erica Rosen

First published in Great Britain in 2000 by Dorling Kindersley Limited,
80 Strand, London WC2R ORL

Copyright © 2000 Dorling Kindersley Limited

2 4 6 8 10 9 7 5 3

ISBN 0-7513-6296-4

Colour reproduction by Colourscan
Printed in Italy by L.E.G.O

Acknowledgements
DK would like to thank Folkmanis Inc. for permission
to photograph the "Furry Folk" hen puppet.
DK would also like to thank Maggie Haden
and Richard Blakey for Milly and Bob.

Can you find the little bear in each scene?

P.B. BEAR
Let's Play Doctor

Lee Davis

One afternoon and his friends were

sharing 🍰 and ☕☕.

"When I grow up," said 🐔 , "I'd like to be

a famous pop star."

"I'd rather be a racing driver,"

"I'd like to be a d

make

found his dressing-up .

"Here's a ✚ for you to wear .

You can be a nurse," he said.

"And this and are just

Doctor," said .

" said .

"Now you need an ," said P.B. Bear.

"Then we can see if the is working."

and drew an of the inside of

Hilda's tummy. "Too much cake," said .

"What's that terrible noise?" said .

"Nee naa nee naa nee naa nee naa!"

The noise was , the driver.

"I've come to take the patient to hospital."

"Watch out for her !" warned .

"Be careful!" shouted . But it was

too late. 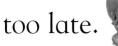 couldn't stop. CRASH!

nose
arm
eye
mouth
paw
tummy

"Now we've got two patients!" said .

"Ouch!" said . "I hurt all over."

"My leg really does hurt now." said .

"We must get you both to the  ,

right away," said .

In hospital  and covered in

a big and stuck a on his beak.

had some more and a .

Soon they were both feeling much better.

"Thank you," said . "A racing driver

needs to have a doctor and nurse as friends!"

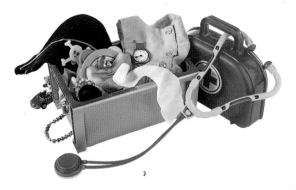

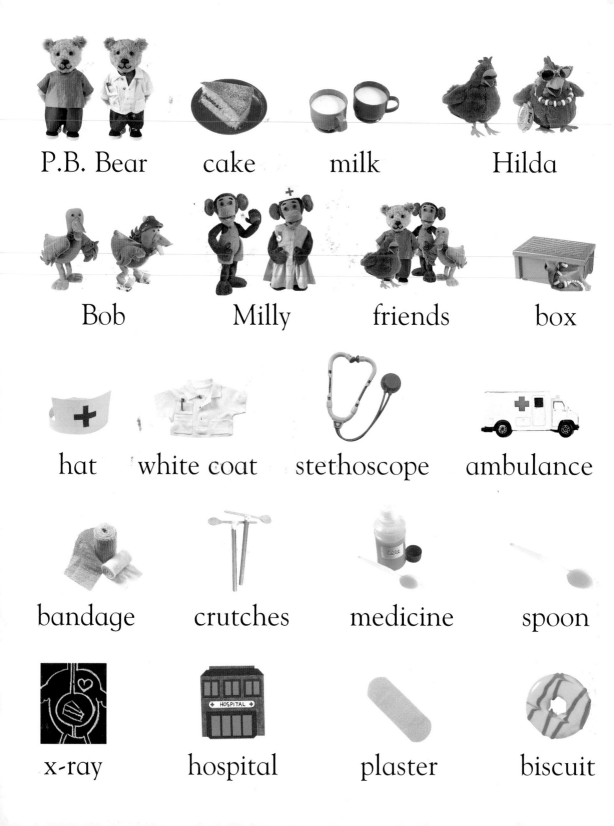

P.B. Bear   cake   milk   Hilda

Bob   Milly   friends   box

hat   white coat   stethoscope   ambulance

bandage   crutches   medicine   spoon

x-ray   hospital   plaster   biscuit